HORRIBLE SCIENCE
TEACHERS' RESOURCES

MICRO-ORGANISMS

Nick Arnold • Tony De Saulles
additional material David Tomlinson

AUTHOR
Nick Arnold

ILLUSTRATIONS
Tony De Saulles

ADDITIONAL MATERIAL
David Tomlinson

EDITOR
Roanne Charles

ASSISTANT EDITORS
Wendy Tse and Catherine Gilhooly

SERIES DESIGNER
Joy Monkhouse

DESIGNERS
Catherine Mason and Erik Ivens

This book contains extracts from *Microscopic Monsters*, *Explosive Experiments* and *The Body Owner's Handbook* in the Horrible Science series. Text © 2001, 2001, 2002, Nick Arnold. Illustrations © 2001, 2001, 2002, Tony De Saulles. First published by Scholastic Children's Books. Additional text © 2006, David Tomlinson.

Designed using Adobe InDesign

Published by Scholastic Ltd
Villiers House
Clarendon Avenue
Leamington Spa
Warwickshire
CV32 5PR

www.scholastic.co.uk

Printed by Bell & Bain Ltd, Glasgow

1 2 3 4 5 6 7 8 9   6 7 8 9 0 1 2 3 4 5

British Library Cataloguing-in-Publication Data
A catalogue record for this book is available from the British Library.

ISBN 0-439-96502-0
ISBN 978-0439-96502-6

TEACHERS' NOTES

Horrible Science Teachers' Resources: Micro-organisms is inspired by the Horrible Science book *Microscopic Monsters*. Each photocopiable page takes a weird and wonderful excerpt from the original, as well as material from *Explosive Experiments* and *The Body Owner's Handbook*, and expands on it to create a class-based teaching activity, fulfilling both National Curriculum and QCA objectives. The activities can be used individually or in a series as part of your scheme of work.

With an emphasis on research, experimentation and interpreting results, the activities will appeal to anyone even remotely curious about the Horrible world around us!

What are micro-organisms?

Micro-organisms are also called microbes or germs. There are three common types. They are: some fungi, viruses and bacteria. Fungi include yeast as well as mushrooms and some moulds. A germ is a harmful micro-organism. Viruses are smaller than bacteria and can cause infectious diseases. Germs can be used to immunise as a mild dose of a disease causes the body to make antibodies which will protect it against a larger dose later. Bacteria can be useful in some food production (such as yoghurt), but can also cause harmful decay and disease. Micro-organisms are often too small to be seen without a microscope.

For guidance on safe microbiology see *Be Safe!* (ASE) and *Studying Micro-organisms in Primary Schools* (CLEAPSS guide L190).

PART 1:
LOOKING CLOSELY

Page 11: Strangely small
Learning objective
To observe surroundings carefully.
To consider that micro-organisms are often too small to be seen.

Start this session by talking about small objects, encouraging the children to suggest ever-smaller things around them. Ask them to use their rulers and see who can find the smallest object in the class. Introduce the concept that some things are so small that we cannot see them. Use photocopiable page 11 to focus on this subject, using any knowledge the children may have about 'germs' and 'bacteria'. Introduce the term 'micro-organism'. Bring the class back together at the end of the session to swap ideas and share information. Compile a class list of questions that the children want to find out about micro-organisms.
Answer: c) At just 0.2mm, a mite is one of the smallest objects anyone can see. Your eyes can't see smaller things because the lenses in your eyeballs can't focus on them. And that means that whatever you look at has a whole lot of detail that's too small to make out. This tiny world can be very incredible, and very beautiful (they say small is beautiful, don't they?).

Page 12: Look again!
Learning objective
To observe surroundings carefully.
To interpret surroundings using scientific observation.

Use this session to develop observation skills. Start by taking an everyday object and describing it in general terms. Hand it to a child and ask him or her to describe a particular feature in detail. Pass the object around in a circle as many times as you can until it has been thoroughly described. Record these observations. Organise children to work in pairs and use photocopiable page 12 to look at a series of objects you have selected. Choose objects with interesting and different textures to encourage close observation and detailed description. Use this activity as the basis for a class observatory display that you can build on as the topic progresses.

Page 13: Lovely lenses
Learning objective
To interpret surroundings using scientific observation.
To understand that a lens can magnify.

Start this session by asking a volunteer to wear a pair of sunglasses. Ask the child to describe the difference that this makes to what he or she can see. Discuss the differences in terms of colour and shade, explaining that this is one use that lenses can have. Ask the children if they can think of other uses for lenses, focusing on why people wear spectacles and contact lenses. (This is also a good opportunity to stamp out any bullying regarding the wearing of glasses.) Use a magnifying glass to demonstrate the use of a lens to see things close up, asking children to describe the difference the lens makes. Use the activity on photocopiable page 13 to develop understanding of how a lens can work, encouraging the children to revisit the Object Observatory from photocopiable page 12 and to contrast the results.

Answer: b) Light bends as it passes through the bottle and the water and the angle the light hits your eye at fools your brain into thinking that the object is much nearer and so much larger than it really is. And that – surprise, surprise – is how a microscope lens works, only the bending of light is done by the glass.

Page 14: Centimetre challenge
Learning objective
To use appropriate measurements in scientific observation.

Introduce your class to scale by using a set of differently sized objects in the classroom. Using a tape measure or ruler and photocopiable page 14, let groups establish just what a single centimetre looks like. Encourage the groups to look in contrasting locations for different things that could fit in a one-centimetre scale, for example from the playground, sandpit, maths cupboard and so on. The challenge should focus on the variety of things that can fit snugly into one centimetre. You can add special categories, such as smallest object, asking how many grass blades fit side by side in one centimetre. Bring the items together for a class exhibition to see what the groups found for the centimetre challenge. Finish with a prize giving ceremony, asking the children to nominate and vote for their favourite entries.

Page 15: Micro-magic
Learning objective
To apply scientific understanding in practical observation.
To choose and use scientific equipment appropriately.

Recap any work you have done about observing small-scale objects and use photocopiable page 15

to prepare the children for using a microscope. Ask them what they expect to see and contrast these answers with what they actually see. Many will observe that it is another mini-world that has gone unnoticed previously – this new world appears before your eyes, like magic! Challenge the children to explain their reasons for choosing certain objects to put under the microscope and encourage collaborative choices and suggestions.

Page 16: The great micro-magic show!
Learning objective
To understand that micro-organisms are all around us.
To understand that we need a microscope to see micro-organisms individually.
To make careful observations and draw conclusions.

Use your microscope to show what a difference a strong lens makes to what we can see. Ask children to predict the view they will get of objects they have prepared on microscope slides and to record these predictions on photocopiable page 16. Contrast these predictions with what they see, recording similarities as well as differences. Discuss how easy or difficult it was to view the objects with a microscope. Which objects were easiest to study and why? Explain that microscope slides often use a dye or stain to make things show up.

Talk about how disclosure tablets use a temporary harmless dye to stain plaque (a sticky colourless film of bacteria and sugars) in the mouth. These tablets show us how easy it is for plaque to develop if we do not brush our teeth thoroughly and have too much sugary foods: areas of dark stains signify plaque build-up. The plaque bacteria eat up sugar and produce acids, which then eat away at the enamel on your teeth! If we clean our teeth carefully these acids are removed and the plaque reduced. The dye should clear within an hour, especially if you eat something crunchy like an apple or carrot and then brush your teeth. They are available from dentists, chemists or often even free from some toothpaste manufacturers!

Try this disclosure tablets experiment as a homework activity. The children have to: predict what will happen when they take a disclosure tablet; record what they use and do; record the results and consider what the results mean. Ensure that the class understands how to use the disclosure tablets and, if necessary, write up notes for the method first. It is best to check parental permission before carrying out this activity. Encourage children to check their teeth in a regular mirror and to carefully record their observations of the effects of the disclosure tablets in writing and with diagrams. This is a good opportunity to stress the importance of brushing your teeth, and to practise good teeth-brushing techniques.

Page 17: Make your own microscope
Learning objective
To choose scientific equipment appropriately.
To understand that a lens can be used to magnify.

Recap any work you have done regarding lenses. Look at a microscope in detail with the children and come to a class agreement on the main design features of a microscope. Use photocopiable page 17 to challenge the children to follow instructions. Then discuss children's ideas of how they could improve on the design, using their own models as a starting point.

Pages 18 & 19: Fascinating forensics 1 & 2
Learning objective
To observe and put these observations into context.

Start this session by talking about clues the children may be familiar with from mystery stories and television dramas, such as fingerprints, DNA, and pieces of clothing. Introduce the word 'forensic'. Encourage children to use their science knowledge about observation and microscopes to solve the mystery on photocopiable page 18. This activity can also provide a useful assessment of what the children have understood so far. Give a team briefing at the beginning and ask for a team reflection on the final theories they have for identifying a culprit. Focus this activity further by setting it up prior to the lesson and leaving clues such as a trainer, a hair or a glove. Use photocopiable page 19 to encourage children to look even closer at the area around them and collect the tiny specs that we may dismiss as 'fluff' or 'dust'.

Page 20: Got any jobs?
Learning objective
To understand that lenses can be used in different ways.
To know that equipment is chosen appropriate to the task.

Use photocopiable page 20 to encourage research of the many different uses of a microscope, particularly

the examination of germs and bacteria. Use the quiz format to encourage extra questions set by different teams in a Microbe Mastermind Team Challenge. **Answers: 2)** It's hard to use a microscope underwater and at the bottom of the sea there isn't enough light to see anything. It would be better to take a bit of rock to the surface and study it there. All the rest are TRUE... **1)** Accident investigators often look at metal from wrecked planes to find cracks and the marks made by strains just before the accident. These may be able to help explain why the accident happened. **3)** The microscope shows how well the diamond has been cut. By the way, if you can't afford diamonds you could study salt grains. Each is a single box-like crystal about 60 micrometres square. But do this at mealtimes and you could be 'a-salted' by your parents! **4)** Like any metal, gold is made up of crystals a few micrometres wide that look like crazy paving. By looking at the shape of the crystals you can tell which are gold and which are junk.

=PART 2:=
MICRO-ORGANISMS UP CLOSE

Page 21: Tiny plants
Learning objective
To understand that micro-organisms are all around us.

Prior to this session collect together a sample of algae (check your fish bowl) and shrubby or leafy lichen (these are most likely to be found on trees). Use a disposable spatula or plastic spoon to scrape the algae from the fish bowl. Do this in front of the children, as it will need to be fresh and hydrated for observation. Present it to them on a paper plate and remind them not to touch these specimens. Ask for observations (smell, colour, form) before putting some on a slide. Contrast the microscope observations with those made earlier on the plate.

Use the fact box on photocopiable page 21 to introduce the idea that there are different sorts of micro-organisms, encouraging the children to describe what they see in this group of tiny plants. Swap observations and encourage suggestions of further examples that can be found.
Safety note: Dispose of the plate, samples and spatula or spoon immediately after use, and remember to wash your hands thoroughly after handling the specimens.

Pages 22 & 23: Alarming algae 1 & 2
Learning objective
To make and contrast observations, leading to an informed conclusion.
To know that micro-organisms feed and grow.

Bring in a houseplant that the children can touch in safety and observe close-up. Establish the conditions that the plant needs to grow and survive, recapping any work you have done on photosynthesis. Encourage different groups to take responsibility for the plant during the week prior to this session. During the session use photocopiable page 22 to record observations on the conditions needed for algae to thrive and those for the houseplant. Discuss why these conditions are so different. Ask children to apply this knowledge to the activity on photocopiable page 23 where they have the opportunity to design their own algae, giving instructions on its perfect habitat and how to care for it!

Page 24: Foul fungi
Learning objective
To make predictions and observations.
To know that micro-organisms feed and grow.

Start this session with a reminder of why we never eat anything in a science lab, no matter how tempting: under no circumstances must any of the objects studied be eaten or licked. Give a clear warning regarding fungi. Back this up with information about toadstools and poisons. Even though some of the objects to be studied are used as foodstuffs we never eat them in scientific study!

Bring in a selection of different mushrooms, dried or fresh, and ask the children to describe what they see. Stress that although these types of fungi may be edible, this is not always the case. Talk about other fungi they may have seen, such as dry rot, fungus on a tree trunk, and toadstools growing wild.

Use an apple core to demonstrate a fungus (mould) growing. Place the apple in a sealed plastic bag with some pin-prick holes in it to allow air in but stop fungal spores getting into the surrounding air. The apple should be left out of reach and in a warm area for quickest results! Use photocopiable page 24 to record the results, encouraging the children to suggest reasons for what is happening.

The time needed for the apple to rot will depend on how the apple has been stored, whether it is organic, market-bought, home-grown or from a supermarket

– as well as the temperature of the classroom. A good average would be to allow a week for serious changes: make daily observations until you feel that the learning objective has been met.
Safety note: NEVER open a bag containing rotting matter. Dispose of it in an external bin.

Pages 25–27: Museum of mould 1–3
Learning objective
To make predictions and observations.
To understand that living things can be broken down by micro-organisms.
To know that micro-organisms feed and grow.
To understand the importance of fair testing.

This mini-project combines practical experimentation, observation and research. You will need a collection of foodstuffs. Fruit are ideal suggestions for the mould experiment on photocopiable pages 25 and 26. (Do not use eggs or meat products.) Photocopiable page 25 focuses on different types of foodstuff and the role microbes play. As a general rule, fungi and bacteria are present in foodstuffs, but humans either eat the food whilst the levels are low or cook it sufficiently to kill off much of the microbes. We also store our food at cold temperatures to slow the eventual takeover by microbes. What the children will see in the main activity is this process of microbes gaining the upper hand – and it does not look pleasant!

The initial research activity on photocopiable page 25 encourages the children to look at how microbes are used in the production of antibiotics, yoghurt, alcohol (yeast), cheese and so on. You can put examples of these in the museum but be careful to acknowledge that these are man-made products as opposed to the natural foods to be observed in the mould experiment. Use photocopiable page 26 to record the changes the children see. The children can handle the original foods but under no circumstances should they touch anything that is rotting.

Photocopiable page 27 focuses on what happened and why, comparing the children's original ideas with their results. Enlarge the page to A3 to give the children plenty of room to draw and observe changes. The foodstuffs in Set A will decay more quickly than those in Set B as their protective skin defences have been cut. Use this as an opportunity to talk about the protective role that skin plays for fruit and vegetables as well as humans! The food will also decay quicker the more it is exposed (unless it dries out and all moisture is removed), hence the comparison between cut and whole foods. Ask children to design their own experiments to test their theories (a particular focus could be the role of temperature in speeding up and slowing down the decaying process).

Page 28: Murderous microbes
Learning objective
To understand the link between microbes and illness. To apply scientific knowledge to their own situation.

Start this session by talking about how we feel when we are unwell. List common symptoms of colds and flu, based on the children's experiences. Also include suggestions about measles and mumps and other viruses that the children are familiar with. Use photocopiable page 28 to focus on the role that different microbes have in the spread and vigour of disease and illness. End the session by talking about how we use immunisation to help combat this threat and how pioneering work by Edward Jenner, eventually has saved millions of lives. Use the children's own experiences of booster jabs, explaining how immunisation works (see 'What are micro-organisms?' on page 3). If you have a reasonably sophisticated class you could also bring up the less positive harnessing of bacteria in the devastating form of germ warfare.

Pages 29 & 30: Bloomin' bacteria 1 & 2
Learning objective
To apply scientific knowledge to their own situation. To choose appropriate methods of presenting information.

Use photocopiable pages 29 and 30 as an assessment of your class's work so far. Photocopiable page 29 allows the children to demonstrate a basic grasp of where bacteria are found and how they can be transferred. Use photocopiable page 30 to focus children on different types of bacteria and to consider the way that we sometimes harness them for specific reasons. For example, 'friendly' bacteria in probiotic products are marketed as having a beneficial effect in the gut. As part of their research, children could investigate the benefits and disadvantages of bacteria working in our body. Use examples of the poster for a display and use photocopiable page 30 to encourage a class campaign and debate, culminating in a vote as to whether, on balance, bacteria are a good thing or not.

Page 31: Boastful bacteria
Learning objective
To present information in a variety of ways.

To expand on where bacteria are found, use photocopiable page 31 to prompt children to look further than their own habitat or fridge! Encourage use of the internet to research ideas and to share these by continuing the cartoon format. These can be added to a class display next to your museum of mould. **Answers: ALL these boasts are TRUE! 1)** Scientists have revived bacteria on plant specimens this old. **2)** Bacteria that live in polluted sea water can eat ships! What happens is bacteria in the water eat the sulphur and turn it into sulphide. This joins to iron atoms on the ship to make a black smelly chemical called iron sulphide. Other bacteria happily guzzle this foul mixture – and eat the ship. **3)** It's true – some bacteria eat tarmac. Mind you, it takes them hundreds of years to do it – it's a bit like you trying to eat a pile of hamburgers the size of Mount Everest! **4)** Bacteria live at the bottom of the sea. But they're so used to the pressure of the water that when they are brought up to the surface where there's less water crushing down on them, their little bodies go pop. **5)** Some bacteria like it hot and they're quite happy in your hot copper pipes. They eat the chemical sulphur in the water and poo out a chemical called sulphide; sulphide joins with copper atoms in the pipes to make a chemical called copper sulphide that makes the water in your hot taps smell of rotten eggs. **6)** Disinfectant contains a chemical called phenol that kills most bacteria – but some bacteria think it's a treat and happily guzzle it!

Page 32: First aid for food
Learning objective
To understand basic good practice in hygiene and handling food.
That micro-organisms live in food and grow.

Start this session by posing the quiz questions at the top of photocopiable page 32. Ask children to give reasons for their choices. Mould is clearly visible but explain that other micro-organisms such as bacteria are also at work when food goes bad. Use the answers from the quiz (given below) to focus on methods of preserving food, leading the children to think about ways to reduce bacteria within food. Use photocopiable page 32 to design posters about food preservation.

Bacteria breakfast quiz answers: a) For some reason bacteria don't eat vitamin C. Maybe they don't like healthy foods? **b)** Some bacteria live happily in weak sulphuric acid and can even eat it! **c)** Bacteria happily scoff latex – a kind of tree gum that is the raw material of rubber. During the Second World War many homes burnt down in air raids because bacteria had eaten holes in the fire hoses. The rubber in wellie boots is treated with sulphur but as you know, some bacteria can eat this chemical. **d)** Angkor in Cambodia is one of the wonders of the world. It's also a giant bacteria snack bar. Bacteria in the soil make sulphide which is drawn up with moisture into the stones of the temple. More bacteria eat the chemical and poo out an acid that eats away the temple.

Could you be a scientist? answer: c) You'll be interested to know that 725 people actually drank the disgusting drink but in 1980 someone accidentally swallowed the toe. I guess that was just toe bad!

Page 33: Manufacturing microbes
Learning objective
To know that micro-organisms feed and grow.
To know that bacteria cause decay.
To carry out practical experiments and observe the results.
To record observations and results accurately.

The idea of actually growing some bacteria may seem revolting, but an experiment like this is the safest way it can be done. Ask children to follow the instructions on photocopiable page 33 carefully, and to explain why they are taking each step, hypothesising what they think will happen. Focus the children on recording the results of their experiment, explaining what they think happened and why. Compare these ideas with the original hypotheses.

Ensure that the containers are cleaned out with care after the experiment: wash them out gently, preferably down an external drain; dispose of the plant material in an external bin; wash hands thoroughly afterwards.

Answer: a) The cloudiness is made by millions of bacteria happily eating the stems. The bacteria were on the flower stems and in the air around the container. Empty the container outside and round up a grown-up to wash it with disinfectant. If **c)** then CONGRATULATIONS, you've discovered a new form of bacteria... Now get out fast!

==== PART 3: ====
EXPERIMENTS AND ASSESSMENT

Page 34: Attack of the amoebas
Learning objective
To present information in a variety of ways.
To know that micro-organisms are living things.

Start this session by talking about the tiny things you have looked at so far in this topic. Ask a research group to use the internet and books to make a presentation about amoebas – where they occur and what they do. Use this presentation alongside photocopiable page 34, aiming for an accurate 3D representation. Finally, refer to any plays or films that the children have seen recently, and divide the class into writers, directors and prop makers to produce a class disaster movie (or in this case disaster play) called 'Attack of the amoebas'. Advise them to use the 'Bet you never knew!' box on the photocopiable sheet as a starting point.

Pages 35–37: The incredible body tour 1–3
Learning objective
To understand that micro-organisms are living things.
To understand basic good practice in hygiene.

Ask the children why we all wash and bathe regularly. Ask how they feel when they are squeaky clean compared to when they feel hot, sweaty, smelly and grubby! Focus on the reason why we must wash and what happens when we don't. Ask the children why we will start to smell, and write down the suggestions. (The build-up of what we call 'dirt' is food, and ideal breeding grounds, for micro-organisms.) Ask the children to use photocopiable page 35 to record what they think the micro-organisms will be doing and where they will be located, before embarking on the incredible body tour (photocopiable pages 35 and 36). Use this information along with additional research and accumulated knowledge to create a human with a hygiene problem on photocopiable page 37. This figure can also be used as the plan for a 3D model of a human body to form a display.

Page 38: House of horrors
Learning objective
To present information in a variety of ways.
To use research as a scientific tool.

Start the session by looking around the classroom, asking children to point out the smallest specks of dust, trampled-in mud, plasticine, pencil shavings and so on that they can find. At the risk of alienating your school caretaker, explain that even when we keep our houses and schools really clean a certain amount of what we call 'dirt' remains. Use photocopiable page 38 and the Erasmus quotation to show what happens when things get really out of hand in the housework department! Ask the children to develop the scenario into a play showing a running battle between Mrs Mopp-Bucket and the micro-organisms in her house. Remind children to use their accumulated science knowledge to give an accurate as well as entertaining representation and to suggest what she could do to keep the micro-organisms under control.

Page 39: Pillow problems
Learning objective
To understand that not all micro-organisms are harmful.
To use a variety of information sources.

Ask the children what happens when we are asleep. Aside from dreams or a nip to the loo it is unlikely that we are aware of anything else. However, our heads are resting on an entire city of activity! Pillows are perfect for micro-organisms. Link this to work you may have done on personal hygiene and home cleanliness; asking the children what they think happens in the pillow. Although these micro-organisms are generally harmless, they can become a real problem if hygiene is neglected, and can be a cause of allergies. Use photocopiable page 39 and the postcard activity to focus on that link, encouraging further research on the internet or from books (or even pillow manufacturers). Share the final postcards at the end of the session before creating a 'Pillow problems (and how to solve them)' display.

Pages 40 & 41: The microbe good food guide 1 & 2
Learning objective
To choose appropriate methods of presenting information.
To use scientific vocabulary correctly.

Start this session by looking at a collection of information leaflets. Ask what common features there are and which are most 'user friendly'. Use the information and activity on photocopiable pages 40 and 41 to assess what the children have understood about how and where microbes can breed, live and transfer from one place to another. Encourage the use of science vocabulary as well as diagrams, and remind the children of what they agreed were the main features of an information leaflet. (Photocopiable page 41 gives basic suggestions to help planning.) Bring all the leaflets together at the end of the session, encouraging self-assessment as well as your own opinion. The class could vote on the best leaflets, copies of which could be distributed as part of a class presentation in an assembly.

Page 42: Yucky yeast 1
Learning objective
To understand that micro-organisms are living things.
To understand that micro-organisms feed and grow.
To carry out practical experiments.
To record observations.

Start this session by introducing the word 'yeast'. Ask the children if they have heard of it and if so, where. Talk about different uses: we eat yeast extract on toast – which is made of bread – which rises because of… yeast. Challenge the children to discover what yeast actually does, explaining that it is a micro-organism. Use photocopiable page 42, asking the children to follow these instructions or observe as you do it:
● Mix a teaspoon of yeast in warm water; add half a teaspoon of sugar, and stir.
● Fill your test tube halfway with this solution.
● Stretch your balloon over the top of the test tube securely (an elastic band may help to prevent slippage).
● Place the balloon in a warm place (over a radiator or in a sunny window) and observe what happens.
At each step, encourage the children to note what is being done, and make a prediction based on their accumulated knowledge. The balloon should inflate to a noticeable degree. Ask the children to research why this happened. (The yeast, sugar and water mixture creates a gas that rises up the test tube and semi-inflates the balloon.)
Safety note: Take care when handling test tubes!

Pages 43 & 44: Yucky yeast 2 & 3
Learning objective
To understand that micro-organisms are living things.
To carry out practical experiments.
To understand the importance of fair testing; presenting information in a variety of ways.

Show the children a dough mixture and a piece of bread. Ask them what they know about the process that goes on in bread making. Aside from kneading and baking, an important part is allowing the dough to 'rise' and this involves yeast microbes working very hard. Use the recipe on photocopiable page 43 to look at how instructions are presented and the order they should go in. The order for the instructions is: d, f, g, a, h, b, c, e. Encourage the children to measure accurately and to keep clear observation records, using photocopiable page 44. Use this dough experiment to talk about comparative testing and the importance of fair conditions. Encourage prediction and hypothesis at each step and compare the results of both tests in order to formulate a class theory about what yeast does to dough. You could repeat this experiment and place the dough balls in a fridge to contrast the effects of temperature.

The data handling on photocopiable page 44 is a useful graphic tool to compare results of the experiments. Some children may find this easier if you enlarge the sheet to A3. Use the final graphs alongside the information tables from the children's original observations to look at how we use different methods to present data.
Safety note: Remind the children that we never eat anything in a science lab!

Page 45: Dreadful decay
Learning objective
To understand that micro-organisms are part of the decaying process.
To record observations and form opinions based on these observations.

Start this session by talking about vegetation the children may have seen 'rotting', linking this to work you have done on bacteria and decay. Talk about why some things rot and others don't. Collect a selection of man-made and natural objects. Good examples are suggested on photocopiable page 45 but you can find local replacements. Ask the children to hypothesise which items will rot and which won't. Place the objects in a bag you have put lots of small holes in.

Bury the bag in a large planter or flowerbed – it only needs to be shallow, marking the site. Give a different team the task of unearthing and reburying the bag each week, ensuring they wear suitable protection on their hands (small food or sandwich bags will do if plastic gloves are too big). Ask the children to record the results and the reasons they think are behind the changes. Some man-made items (the metal can) will not rot; others that are made with natural material (such as a paper-based exercise book) will. Ask the children how they think micro-organisms are involved and to make a presentation of their ideas.
Safety note: Wash hands thoroughly after handling the bag. Do not open or touch the contents of the bag, especially if it contains anything that is rotting, and dispose of it safely in an external bin.

Pages 46 & 47: Beware of the bathroom 1 & 2
Learning objective
To present information in a variety of ways.
To understand basic good practice in hygiene.

Ask the children what we must always do when we have been to the toilet: wash our hands. Sadly this is not always a universal habit amongst many primary age children so be prepared for other suggestions too! Link the correct answer to the work you have already done on micro-organisms, personal hygiene and home hygiene. Use photocopiable pages 46 and 47 to encourage the children to share their knowledge in an assembly or to make a class display.
Answer: c) Probably – or as a scientist would say... 'yes and no.'

Page 48: Mixed-up microbes quiz
Learning objective
To use scientific vocabulary accurately.

Give the children a puzzle: mix up the letters of your own name into an anagram if possible, and challenge them to work out what it is. Encourage the children to do the same with their names; it doesn't matter if they can't make other words from the letters. Now ask the children to un-jumble the letters in the quiz on photocopiable page 48 to find each answer. Encourage children to add their own questions about micro-organisms using the science vocabulary they have learned in this topic.

NAME _____   DATE _____

Strangely small

Which of these is the smallest?
a) Your pocket money.
b) Your teacher's brain.
c) A mite (a bug that looks like a scaled-down spider).

● There are small things all around us ... terrifyingly tiny in fact!

● Write a list of tiny terrors you want to find out about.

Tiny terrors

_____

_____

_____

_____

● What do you already know about these situations and the micro-organisms that live in them?

_____

_____

_____

_____

_____

_____

Millions of creatures *die* when you walk on the grass.

Flushing the toilet can cover you in *poo*.

Slimy animals lurk between your *teeth*.

NAME _____ DATE _____

LOOK AGAIN!

You're holding a *microscope* ... a wonderful instrument for peering at tiny objects and seeing them like no human eye ever can. A device for making things appear hundreds of times larger than they really are...

What's that? This sheet doesn't look like a microscope? Oh, but I'm telling you it *is* – try putting your eye up close to this circle. Look closely...

Concentrate hard ... very hard ... see anything?

Well, look below and prepare to be amazed. Thanks to the power of this sheet ... er, I mean microscope, we are now looking at the sheet enlarged 100 times.

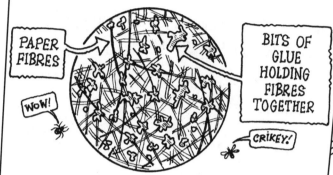

So you know that paper is made up of little fibres that were once wood from trees? Well, here's your chance to check out what else you know...

● Now take a look at your Object Observatory and sketch what you see.

How we see the object every day	My close-up observation

NAME _____ DATE _____

Lovely lenses

In around 1300 someone in Italy (no one knows who!) found out how to grind glass to make lenses. The trick was getting the right shape – wanna know how it's done? Well, why not make your own? Go on, it's easy!

Dare you discover ... how to make your own lens?

In the olden days you had to cut the glass carefully to shape and then grind it with gritty substances by hand until you had made exactly the right curve. And then you had to 'polish' it to get rid of any scratches. (Basically, this meant grinding the glass some more with fine powders.) This grinding might take days of toil.

But you'll be pleased to know there's an easier way...

What you need:
A bottle shaped like this…
(An empty mouthwash bottle is ideal.)

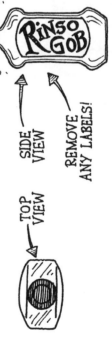

TOP VIEW

SIDE VIEW

REMOVE ANY LABELS!

RINSO GOB

What you do:
1 Completely fill the bottle with water so there are no air bubbles.
2 Place the bottle sideways on over this sheet, put your eye close to the bottle and look at this fascinating blood-sucking flea.

HURRY UP, I HAVEN'T GOT ALL DAY!

You should be able to see that the flea has got bigger – but how? Here's a clue: you have to imagine light bouncing off the page and bouncing into your eyeballs.

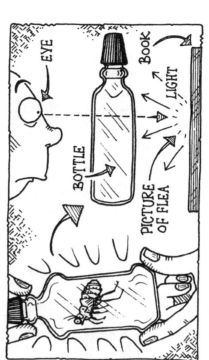

EYE

BOTTLE

PICTURE OF FLEA

Book

LIGHT

Which of these explanations is correct:
a) The light speeds up as it passes through water and this makes your brain think the flea is bigger than it is.
b) The water bends the light towards a point. If I put my eye at this point I can see the flea close up.
c) The water makes the light brighter and this makes my brain think that the flea is bigger.

● Now use your lens to look at the objects in your Observatory. What do you notice?

NAME _____ DATE _____

Centimetre challenge

● You can fit a lot into a centimetre! Take a look at this enlargement...

YOUR THUMBNAIL IS ABOUT 1 CM = 10,000 MICROMETRES

MITE IS 0.2 MM = 200 MICROMETRES

THICKNESS OF A BUBBLE/WIDTH OF A HAIR = 50 MICROMETRES

SPECK OF DUST/PIECE OF GRIT = 20-30 MICROMETRES

WOW, THAT'S SMALLER THAN MY BRAIN!

10,000 MICROMETRES IS 1 CM

BACTERIA = 1-10 MICROMETRES

VIRUS = 17-100 NANOMETRES = LESS THAN ONE TENTH OF A MICROMETRE.

THE LARGEST ATOM = 0.5 NANOMETRES — THAT'S 100 TIMES SMALLER THAN A VIRUS. (BY THE WAY, ATOMS ARE THE TINY BALLS OF MATTER THAT MAKE UP EVERYTHING IN THE UNIVERSE.)

SPACE DUST IN RAINDROP = 2 MICROMETRES

● Look around you. What can you find to fit into a centimetre?
● Draw your suggestions below, actual size!

1 CM

NAME _____   DATE _____

Micro-magic

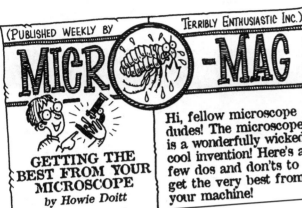

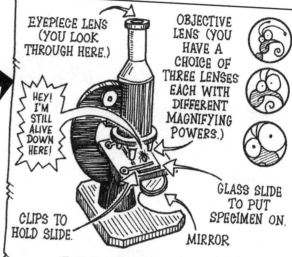

● Make a list of observation objects for your own micro-magic show!

_____

_____

_____

_____

_____

_____

_____

_____

_____

_____

_____

_____

_____

_____

_____

NAME _____   DATE _____

The great micro-magic show!

● How do your objects look?

Object	My prediction	My observation

WOW! THIS ANT LOOKS HUGE! INCREDIBLE! AMAZING!

SAD!

LEEUWENHOEK'S

☠ HORRIBLE HEALTH WARNING!

Don't you try cutting *your* specimens! You might end up examining an interesting slice of fingertip!

Bet you never knew!
How scientists make slides of specimens...
1 They stain the specimen so it shows up really clearly under the microscope. A stain is a special dye that colours certain chemicals and shows up certain parts of the tiny object the scientist is looking at. A commonly used stain is cochineal – made from ground-up beetles!

2 They cut a thin slice of the object. That's so that the light can shine through it from below and you can see it clearly under the microscope. How thin? Well about one thousandth of a millimetre (one micrometre) will do. Scientists use a tool called a microtome to do the cutting – and I expect very mean scientists use it to cut cake.

● Bacteria is all around – and in – us but you can't see it. Use disclosure tablets to show up the bacteria found in our mouths! Write up your experiment, with diagrams, on a separate piece of paper using these headings:

WHAT WE WANTED TO DISCOVER

PREDICTION   METHOD   EQUIPMENT

RESULTS   CONCLUSION

● Use this space to note down important things to remember about disclosure tablets.

SPECIMEN

THE BLADE IS MADE FROM VERY SHARP GLASS (ITS CUTTING EDGE IS SHARPER THAN METAL)

HANDLE

RIGHT, THAT'S ONE MICROMETRE FOR YOU AND THE REST FOR ME!

3 They place the specimen on a glass slide with a drop of water to stop it drying out and a thin piece of glass called a cover slip to protect it. Or if they want to store the specimen they might cover it in glycerine and gelatine and seal the edges of the cover slip with gum arabic to stop it from drying or rotting.

NAME _____   DATE _____

MAKE YOUR OWN MICROSCOPE

● Follow these instructions to make your own microscope – you can examine something else instead of a spider!

Dare you discover ... how to build your own microscope?

What you need:

A specimen to study.

FASCINATING DEAD SPIDER

A piece of card
   (2.5cm wide by 5cm long).
A piece of cellophane (try using the clear wrapping from a greetings card).
Scissors.
Sticky tape.
Pencil or hole punch.
A cardboard tube from a kitchen roll.

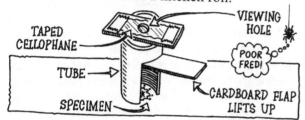

TAPED CELLOPHANE — TUBE → SPECIMEN — VIEWING HOLE — POOR FRED! — CARDBOARD FLAP LIFTS UP

What you do:

1 Use the hole punch or pencil point to make a hole 5mm across in the centre of the card.
2 Cover the hole with cellophane and secure with sticky tape.
3 Cut a length of tube 5cm long and then cut two slots into it, 3cm long and 2.5cm apart, coming down from one end. Lift up the cardboard between the slots to make a little window – make sure it lets in enough light to see what is inside the tube. Place the tube on top of the spider and place the card on top of the tube.
4 Pick up a drop of water on the tip of the pencil and let it fall over the cellophane covering the hole. Make sure the drop covers the hole.
5 Hold your eye very close to the drop and look through it. You should see the spider's eight eyes and fangs in fascinating close up detail. Just don't let it give you nightmares afterwards!

● How could the design be improved? Note your ideas here and then draw your design.

NAME _____ DATE _____

Fascinating forensics 1

There's a whole branch of police work called forensic science that uses microscopes to search for clues to crimes. Here are some forensic clues that we've borrowed from a police museum.

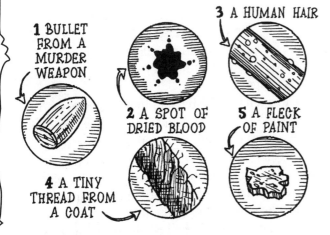

1 BULLET FROM A MURDER WEAPON

3 A HUMAN HAIR

2 A SPOT OF DRIED BLOOD

5 A FLECK OF PAINT

4 A TINY THREAD FROM A COAT

And here's how these clues can catch a villain...
Microscopic monsters fact file

NAME: Forensic science

THE BASIC FACTS: Forensic scientists check the scene of a crime for tiny clues.

THE VICTIM SEEMS TO HAVE BEEN HOLDING A BOWL OF, ER, TOMATO SOUP AT THE TIME OF THE SHOOTING...

1 Scratches on the side of the bullet might match grooves in the barrel of the suspect's gun – who said science isn't groovy?

2 Blood can be tested for DNA. This substance – known as deoxyribo-nucleic acid (de-oxy-ri-bo new-clay-ick acid) – forms a unique chemical code in all of us. If DNA from the victim is found on the murder suspect then chances are they did it.

3 The hair could be matched in colour and microscopic detail to the suspect or victim.

4 The microscopic thread could be matched to a coat worn by the suspect.

5 The paint could be matched to a car driven by the suspect.

MONSTROUS DETAILS: Some forensic evidence is very horrible indeed. Would you fancy looking through a microscope at a pool of sick left at a crime scene to find out the exact foods eaten by a suspect? It's all in a day's work for a forensic scientist!

SWEETCORN, MUSHROOMS AND . . . CATFOOD. INTERESTING!

- Imagine the scene... You arrive at school as usual, your teacher walks into the classroom and... the computer is missing!

- How can you use forensic science to solve this terrible crime?

My forensic investigation

NAME _____   DATE _____

Fascinating forensics 2

Could you be a forensic detective?
Here's an easy experiment to try ...

Dare you discover ... how to collect fibres?
What you need:
A piece of sticky tape.

What you do:
Press the sticky tape firmly on the carpet and then lift it up.

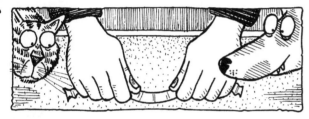

What do you notice?

> **Answer:**
> The tape is covered with carpet fibres which you can examine with your microscope. If you're lucky, you'll find a few human hairs or hairs from the dog or cat. This technique is used by forensic scientists to collect fibres from a crime scene. If they're found on the clothes of a suspect then this could link the suspect with the crime.

The magic microscope
Here are samples of polyester and cotton cut from two pairs of underpants…

Look identical, don't they? Well, let's look closer through the magic microscope…

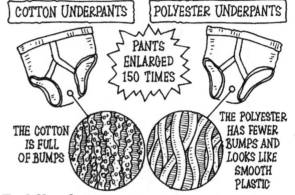

COTTON UNDERPANTS   POLYESTER UNDERPANTS

PANTS ENLARGED 150 TIMES

THE COTTON IS FULL OF BUMPS

THE POLYESTER HAS FEWER BUMPS AND LOOKS LIKE SMOOTH PLASTIC

Foul fibre facts
1 Cotton fibres come from the outer layer of seed cases on the cotton plant and they're never perfectly smooth. Polyester fibres begin life as a plastic substance that's squeezed through a tube so they're smooth and regular.
2 We've been looking at clean underwear. Seen through the microscope, dirty underwear hides all kinds of horrors. The fibres look like tangled spaghetti with lumps of brown stuff and cornflakes in it. The brown stuff is ... no, you're wrong, it's tiny bits of dirt and the "cornflakes" are lumps of dead skin.
3 Take a look at your jeans and you'll see tiny specks of white. In fact, half the threads in your blue jeans are actually white! The blue threads are dyed with indigo and if every thread was this colour the jeans would be bright blue. The white threads give the jeans a "washed 'n' faded" appearance.
4 Wool comes from sheep. Oh, so you knew that? Well, stop bleating – the fibres in wool are sheep hair and like your own hair they're made of a substance called keratin. Enlarged 1000 times through a microscope you can see tiny scales of hair like shiny crazy paving.

● What did you find on your forensic search? Draw close-ups and label them.

Tape 2

Tape 1

Tape 3

NAME _____   DATE _____

Got any jobs?

- What else do we use a microscope for?
- Use books and the internet to help your research.

What I discovered

Here are some exciting jobs that require a microscope. And just to make the quiz even more interesting, we've added a job for which the microscope is as sensible as a pair of exploding underpants – can you spot it?

1 Looking for the causes of a plane crash.

GET THE MICROSCOPES OUT, FRED!

2 Studying rocks at the bottom of the sea.

FASCINATING!

3 Checking the quality of diamonds.

NEXT!

4 Looking at gold to make sure that it's 100 per cent gold and not mixed with some cheaper metal.

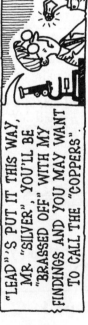

"LEAD"'S PUT IT THIS WAY, MR "SILVER", YOU'LL BE "BRASSED OFF" WITH MY FINDINGS AND YOU MAY WANT TO CALL THE "COPPERS".

NAME _____   DATE _____

TINY PLANTS

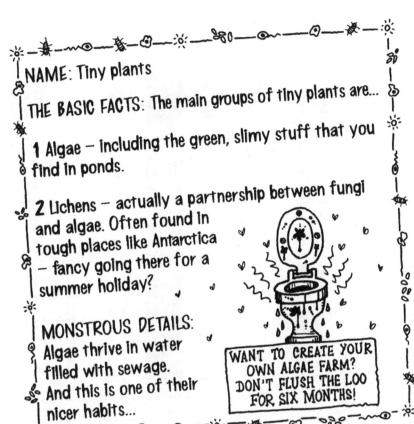

NAME: Tiny plants

THE BASIC FACTS: The main groups of tiny plants are...

1 Algae – including the green, slimy stuff that you find in ponds.

2 Lichens – actually a partnership between fungi and algae. Often found in tough places like Antarctica – fancy going there for a summer holiday?

MONSTROUS DETAILS:
Algae thrive in water filled with sewage. And this is one of their nicer habits...

WANT TO CREATE YOUR OWN ALGAE FARM? DON'T FLUSH THE LOO FOR SIX MONTHS!

● Take a look at your science sample collection. What do you see?

● Draw and record your observations... down to the tiniest detail!

	Looking at it with the naked eye	Looking at it with a microscope
Algae		
Lichens		

NAME _____   DATE _____

Alarming algae 1

To stop your pets multiplying too much, why not use an animal that looks like a plant? It's wild and wacky...

3 Hungry hydra
Description: A green rubber glove.

ARGHHH!
OUCH!

Size: 1.25mm

Cute features: Stinging threads in its fingers kill anything that comes near. Er, that's not too cute, is it?
Feeding: "Fingers" grab the prey and bring it into the creature's mouth.

● Take a close look at the information for 1 and 3 above. What conditions do most algae need to live?

● Contrast this with the conditions your plant needs in order to survive.

● Find as many common needs and differences as you can.

	Algae	My plant
Needs in order to survive		
Does not need		

ALGAE-PALS PET SHOP

SPLIT! SPLIT!
SLITHER!
SLITHER!
SPLIT!

Are you a lonely scientist? Are you seeking a little friend, someone who will listen to your latest scientific theories without falling asleep? Look no further! To order ~ give us a ring and give us your money!

•°•°• WARNING! •°•°•
Algae breed by splitting in half. You might need your pets before they form a vast, slimy mass that poisons their water... and *you* if you fall in!

1 Cute ceratium (ser-rat-tee-um)
Description: Looks like a homemade Christmas decoration that's gone wrong.

CHEERS!

Size: 0.5mm

Cute features: Dagger-like spikes for protection from other microscopic creatures.
Feeding: Don't worry about feeding them – they use sunlight and carbon dioxide gas in the air to make sugar for food – a process called photosynthesis (as if you didn't know!).
Note: you can use your pet as a thermometer. The warmer the water, the more they stick their spikes out. This can be useful for working out if your bath is the right temperature!

2 Delightful diatoms
Description: Indescribable – pretty aren't they?

OOH, D'YOU REALLY THINK SO?

Size: 0.2mm

Delightful features: They shine in the light because they have see-through bodies and hard box-like outer bodies that contain silica, which also makes up sand and glass.
Feeding: Photosynthesis.

NAME _____   DATE _____

My Pet Algae

Alarming algae 2

ALGAE-PALS PET SHOP

Are you a lonely scientist?
Are you seeking a little
friend, someone who
will listen to your latest
scientific theories
without falling asleep?
Look no further!
To order ~ Give us a
ring and give us
your money!

SLITHER!
SPLIT!
SLITHER!
SPLIT!

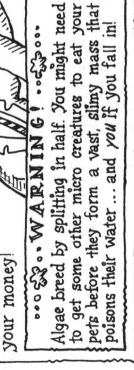

...❀... **WARNING !** ...✿...

Algae breed by splitting in half. You might need
to get some other micro creatures to eat your
pets before they form a vast, slimy mass that
poisons their water ... and *you* if you fall in!

- Use your knowledge about algae and what they need to survive to design your own specimen.

- Draw your pet algae and give details about its size, features, habitat, feeding habits and reproduction.

- Add an owner's manual, showing how to care for the algae when a lucky person gets it from the pet shop!

NAME _____   DATE _____

FOUL FUNGI

THE FUNGI GUIDE TO ETIQUETTE

by Madame Mould

IF YOU DESIRE TO BE ACCEPTED IN THE BEST HOUSES THEN ETIQUETTE IS ESSENTIAL — SO MIND YOUR MANNERS, MOULDS!

TABLE MANNERS
Eating is very important for fungi – so make sure you eat as much as you can whenever you can. (It's acceptable to burp gas afterwards.)

MUNCH! NIBBLE! SCOFF! CHEW! BURP!

BURP!

Four things not to do
NEVER...
● Ask permission before eating.
● Say "please" or "thank you".
● Ask for a second helping – just help yourself anyway.
● Leave the table (before you've eaten it).

Two things to do
ALWAYS...
● Be prepared to eat anything – glue in wallpaper, metal in paints, wood, plaster. Fussy fungi are considered ill-mannered.
● Tell bacteria to back off. A good way to do this is to spray out substances that kill most bacteria like carbon dioxide or hydrogen cyanide. Yes, KILL THEM! I am sure that your hosts will approve of your thoughtfulness!

ARGH!

● Try this experiment to observe how a fungus (mould) takes over an apple as it is left to decay. This is what you need to do:

1 Put an apple core in a clear plastic food bag. Put pin-pricks in the bag to let air in (but the fungi can't get out).

2 Put the bag containing the apple core on a plate or in a bigger container and draw a picture of the apple core. This will be Observation Day 1.

3 Place the bag in a warm place that is usually out of reach (so you can't knock it over by accident!).

4 Observe the apple core every day for about a week and draw and/ or describe what it looks like. Is it changing? Why do you think this is happening?

● Use these headings when writing up your experiment and record your observations using diagrams to show how the apple changed:

WHAT I WANT TO DISCOVER
WHAT I THINK WILL HAPPEN
EQUIPMENT
METHOD
RESULTS
WHAT I DISCOVERED

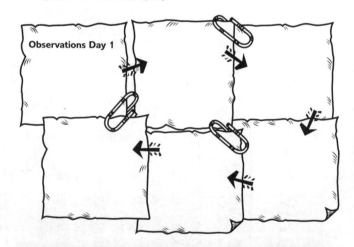

Observations Day 1

Important safety note!
You can look at but NEVER touch anything that is rotting! Ask your teacher to get rid of the apple in the bag – do not try to do this yourself.

NAME _____   DATE _____

Museum of mould 1

● Micro-organisms (or microbes) can grow on lots of different foods. Sometimes we call it mould. What do you know about mould? What causes it?

Usually we throw away things that have become 'mouldy' but sometimes we encourage it!

● Research these microbe key words.

Penicillin _____

Yoghurt _____

Quorn _____

Alcohol _____

Cheese (especially blue cheese!)

_____

The museum of mould is different from any other you have visited because the exhibits are alive and changing... in front of your eyes!

● Try this experiment from the museum.

You will need: a selection of foods, sealable plastic bags with pin-prick holes, a knife and a cutting board.

1 Cut one set of foods in half. Call it 'Set A'. Do not cut the other set of foods. Call it 'Set B'.
2 Put Set A in a plastic bag that has pin-pricks in it and call it 'Observatory 1'.
3 Do the same with Set B and label it 'Observatory 2'.
4 Check the exhibits daily, they could be changing behind your back!

● Draw them as they are at the beginning of the experiment.

Observatory 1: Set A (cut)	Observatory 2: Set B (uncut)

● What do you think will happen?

NAME _____   DATE _____

Museum of mould 2: They're changing!

● Use this observation check sheet to record the changing exhibits!

	Observatory 1: Set A (cut)	Observatory 2: Set B (uncut)
Week 1		
Week 2		
Week 3		

● What is happening?

_____

● Why do you think this is?

_____

● Is it what you expected to happen?

_____

_____

CAUTION!
Do not touch rotting food!

NAME _____   DATE _____

Museum of mould 3

● Take a last look around your museum. What does it look like now?

● Compare it with the pictures you drew when you started. What do you notice?

● In groups, look at the exhibits, asking these questions and any others you can think of.

● The museum loves to receive customer feedback. Complete the form, using your group's answers.

● Did cutting the foods in half make a difference?
● What differences did you observe?
● What is causing this difference?
● How did you keep your test fair?
● What else could you have changed?

Museum of mould

What changed over the three weeks

_____

What we could have changed

_____

What I want to know next

_____

REMEMBER!
Do not touch rotting food!

NAME _____   DATE _____

MURDEROUS MICROBES

NAME: Microbes

THE BASIC FACTS: The main microbes are... Bacteria, Protozoa, Viruses.

1 Bacteria are very tiny and come in all shapes and sizes.

PROTOZOA FIRES PARALYZING CHEMICAL AT BACTERIA

ERK!

BURP!

2 Protozoa change their body shape as they move and engulf bacteria. So if you're tiny don't ask one to come "around" for lunch.

3 Viruses are even smaller so you'll need an electron microscope to spot one. They're basically bundles of DNA.

FLU VIRUS
Attacks cells in the throat (can be a pain in the neck).

MONSTROUS DETAILS: All three can cause deadly diseases.

1 Bacteria cause diseases such as the plague and the lung disease TB.

COUGH!

SWEAT!

2 Protozoa cause malaria – a killer disease which is spread by mosquitoes.

YELLOW!

3 Viruses cause disease by breaking into cells and forcing them to make new viruses until the cells die of exhaustion. Diseases caused by viruses include yellow fever and flu.

Feeling unwell? Maybe it's the microbes!

● Use the internet and books to help you to collect a jail full of germs.

Jail of germs

Picture						
Description of symptoms they cause						

NAME _____   DATE _____

Bloomin' bacteria 1

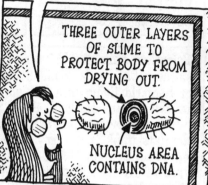

These bacteria look scary!

● How can we avoid getting sick?

● Design a poster to remind people what they can do to bust bacteria.

NAME _____ DATE _____

Bloomin' bacteria 2

 SO HOW MANY TYPES OF BACTERIA ARE THERE? — Lots

 CAN YOU BE MORE EXACT? — No

Scientists from the University of Southern California found 61 types of bacteria living in a hot spring in Yellowstone National Park. 57 were unknown to science. Some scientists think that every pinch of soil could contain 10,000 different types of bacteria but they haven't got round to counting them all yet.

 Any volunteers to count them?

Although, we're talking awfully big numbers. An average-sized lawn holds countless billions of individual bacteria — about 4.5 kg (10 lbs) by weight. And they're eaten by an army of tiny creatures such as protozoa and slimy nematode worms with no eyes and six rubbery lips.

 WHERE ELSE DO BACTERIA LIVE?

Where don't they live! Most bacteria live in "cities" of slime in massive piles like tower blocks 200 micrometres high (that's BIG by their standards). Favourite places for slime cities are — are you ready for this? — sewage pipes, false teeth, contact lenses, the guts and just about anywhere else you can imagine...

 SO WHAT DO BACTERIA DO ALL DAY?

Well, they eat and divide to make new bacteria and they eat and divide and when they're bored of that they divide and eat. Well, I suppose they could play football under the microscope but then they might be caught off-slide! Ha, ha — sorry, just my little joke.

 MUNCH! SPLIT! MUNCH! MUNCH! SPLIT! SPLIT!

- But are all bacteria bad? Use the internet, books and your science knowledge to research and argue your point of view.

- Design a badge and leaflet to support your campaign for or against bacteria.

My badge

My leaflet

NAME _____   DATE _____

Boastful bacteria

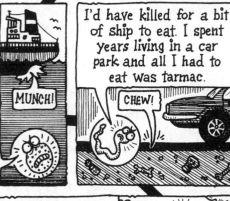

Of course, we had it tough when I were a lad. I was stuck for 300 years in a grain of soil stuck to a dried plant... YAWN!

That's nothing. I remember when I was living on the bottom of a ship and all I had to eat was ... the ship. MUNCH!

I'd have killed for a bit of ship to eat. I spent years living in a car park and all I had to eat was tarmac. CHEW!

Well, of course when I was younger I spent 3,000 years living at the bottom of the sea in the freezing cold with enough water pressing down from above to crush a human flat. SHIVER!

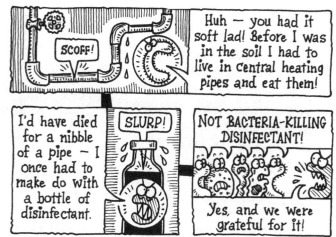

SCOFF! Huh — you had it soft lad! Before I was in the soil I had to live in central heating pipes and eat them!

I'd have died for a nibble of a pipe — I once had to make do with a bottle of disinfectant. SLURP!

NOT BACTERIA-KILLING DISINFECTANT! Yes, and we were grateful for it!

● These bacteria all think they're tough, but do you think their boasts are true?

● Where else are bacteria found? Continue the cartoon.

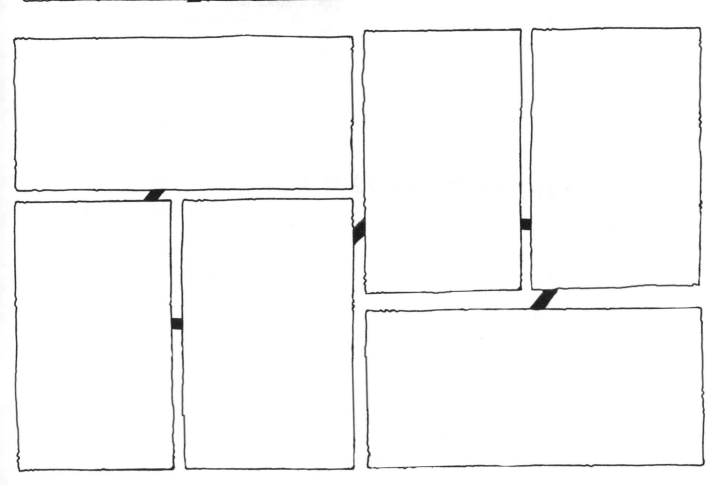

NAME _____ DATE _____

First aid for food

Bacteria breakfast quiz
Which of these "foods" would bacteria
NOT fancy for breakfast...?
a) Your mum's bottle of vitamin C pills.
b) A bucket of sulphuric acid.
c) An old pair of wellie boots.
d) An ancient temple.

● What can we do to prepare, preserve and
serve food to avoid the brilliant bacteria's
plans to get at it first?

Could you be a scientist?
The landlord of a bar in the Yukon, Canada offered
his guests a disgusting cocktail. It was champagne
... with a human toe in it complete with toenail. (The
toe had been found in a log cabin – no one knew
what it was doing there but I expect it was trying to
find its feet.) Anyway, the landlord challenged his
customers to drink the concoction saying:

You can drink it fast, you can drink it slow — but the lips have got to touch the toe!

ARGH!

But why didn't bacteria eat the toe and make
it rot?
a) It was too revolting even for bacteria.
b) It was so cold in the Yukon that the
bacteria froze.

c) The toe had been
pickled in alcohol
and few bacteria
can live in these
conditions.

FOOD SAFETY FIRST!

NAME _____   DATE _____

MANUFACTURING MICROBES

Here's your chance to grow your own microbes!

● Follow the instructions on the right and record your observations below.

Day 1

Day 2

Day 3

Day 4

Day 5

Day 6

Dare you discover ... how to provide a snug, cosy home for microbes?
What you need:
A clear plastic container.
Some beautiful flowers for your teacher so you get a good report.
Water.

What you do:
1 Fill the container halfway with water, measuring how much you put in.
2 Arrange the flowers so your teacher thinks they look beautiful.
3 Put a mark where the water level is.
4 Leave in a warm place and top up the water to the marked level over the next week.

What do you notice? (Concentrate on the water and stems – don't worry about the flower heads!)
a) The liquid has gone cloudy.
b) The liquid has gone green.
c) The liquid has gone frothy and orange and is escaping from the container and eating everything in sight.

Day 7

Bet you never knew!
Methane is made inside cows by bacteria that live in the cow's stomach and digest the tough cell walls of grass. The cow can then digest the grass more easily. Cows get rid of the methane in huge burps or farts. The cows don't mean to be rude but there's no udder choice.

NAME _____   DATE _____

Attack of the amoebas

You needed a microscope to see amoebas and protozoa close-up... until now!

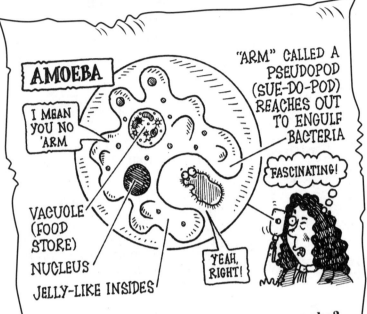

AMOEBA

I MEAN YOU NO 'ARM

"ARM" CALLED A PSEUDOPOD (SUE-DO-POD) REACHES OUT TO ENGULF BACTERIA

FASCINATING!

VACUOLE (FOOD STORE)

NUCLEUS

JELLY-LIKE INSIDES

YEAH, RIGHT!

Bet you never knew!
Protozoa can breed very fast. For example, paramecium (pa-ra-me-see-um) divides every 22 hours. If one started splitting on New Year's Day, by 7 March it would have formed a huge slimy ball 1.6km (one mile) across. Little more than a month later it would have grown to the size of the Earth! Fortunately, other tiny creatures are public-spirited enough to eat the paramecia before they take over the world!

WELL, I WISH THE TINY CREATURES WOULD EAT A BIT FASTER!

OOER!

ERK!

ARGH!

Dare you discover ... how to make an amoeba?
What you need:
A paper hankie (not a snotty one).
That's it.

What you do:
1 Make two tears 4cm long in each side of the hankie. (This will help to make an amoeba-like shape in the water.)
2 Screw the hankie up tightly.
3 Twist any sticking out points of hankie into points to make an amoeba shape.
4 Put it in water. If you stir the water around your amoeba will appear to move. BEWARE, it might engulf your finger!

- Use your model and this information to write your play 'Attack of the amoebas'. Think about what would happen if microbes took over Earth.

- Check that the science facts are correct.

- Set your first scene on New Year's Day... and your last on 7 March!

- Write notes for your play here:

```



```

NAME _____   DATE _____

The incredible body tour 1

● Imagine you've been shrunk small enough to go on a tour inside the human body! What will you see? What scale will it be?

● The information on the right tells you about microbes in your hair and on your skin. Write down what you think microbes will be up to *inside* your body...

● Are you ready for the tour? Here goes!

THE INCREDIBLE BODY TOUR...
HORRIBLE SCIENCE and
Bacteria Breakaways present...
The get away from it all (but not very far) tour
It's the ultimate mini-break on

THE HUMAN SKIN & HAIR!

"I had a rotten time and enjoyed every minute of it" A. Bacterium.

ITINERARY

DAY ONE
Morning: First stop is the mouth for a quick tour of the tongue. Marvel at the sight of 9,000 tastebuds in clusters, some with round tops like mushrooms

and others pointed and ideal for moving food around. Enjoy the sight of the playful local bacteria frolicking amongst the tastebuds!

Afternoon: Sign up for the fascinating microbe safari. Watch the different bacteria in between the teeth. But beware – amoebas lurk in this area and they might try to eat you!

NOTES

1 Chinese leader Mao Tse-tung (1893-1976) never brushed his teeth and they eventually turned green. Eek by gum, I bet Mao just had to green and bear it.

2 The amoebas eat bacteria and are harmless to humans. One place to get a free amoeba is a dog's mouth. When a friendly dog gives you a big slobbery kiss you get an amoeba thrown in too.

DAY TWO

Morning: Enjoy a relaxing walking tour of the skin! Carefully does it – in some teenagers the skin pumps out half a bucket of oil a day so the going might get a bit slippery! Feel free to snack on the delicious oil and any dead bits of skin you might find.

Afternoon: Admire the volcanoes on the face plain. Well, they're not really volcanoes, they're pimples – so watch out when they erupt pus!

NAME _____   DATE _____

The incredible body tour 2

Evening: Slake your thirst at the sweat gland cocktail bar. The local tipple (sweat) is a great tonic for us bacteria. It's full of delicious salts and sugars and minerals to keep us healthy!

— NOTE —
With more than two million sweat bars you're spoilt for choice but beware - women make nice easy-to-drink little sweat droplets, but men can make giant globules that splash onto the floor!

DAY THREE

Morning: Explore the enchanting hair forest. There's always something new to see – like exciting split ends that look like splintered wood or the cute new hairs that look like pink worms emerging from the soil. Let's hope it's not a bad hair day!

SPOOKY!

GUZZLE!

Lunch: Dine on delicious fresh dandruff washed down with fatty oil from the hair.

Afternoon: Admire the fine collection of dust and pollen sticking to the oil on the hair tree trunks. (It's the oil that gives unwashed hair that lovely greasy shine.) If we're particularly lucky we might see some nits (louse eggs) or that shy retiring creature, the human head louse, with its hairy body, jointed legs and feelers and crab-like shell. Unforgettable!

LOOK, OVER THERE!

Evening: That's the end of the tour. Time to hop off the skin and take an air tour of the house before landing on the cat.

WEEEE!
Hop!

More tours

CORNEA
LENS
COOL!

1 THE EYEBALL CELLS EXPERIENCE
Feast your eyes on the cornea with its patchwork of cells like a tiled roof. Seeing is believing as you'll see with the see-through cells of the lens arranged in lines like a venetian blind. (If they weren't see-through the human would be blind instead!)

2 THE BONE BREAKAWAY
Tour the eerie world inside the bones. The spongy bone inside the hard outer layer is like an immense cave system full of inter-connecting tunnels. You'd be a bone-head to miss it!

WHERE ARE YOU?
OVER HERE!

3 THE LONG LUNG WEEKEND
Visit the lungs for a breath of fresh air! Explore the tiny tubes into which air flows and admire the alveoli. These are the bags 0.01 cm (0.004 inches) across surrounded with blood vessels where oxygen goes into the blood and carbon dioxide flows out! Bags of fun for all the family!

HEY MUM, LOOK AT ME!

WARNING: The walls of the tubes are lined with snot and you risk being stuck and then coughed up!

● Write a thank-you note to the microbes for their hospitality. Tell them which bits of the tour were the most interesting.

Thank You

NAME _____   DATE _____

The incredible body tour 3

● Use this outline to pinpoint where
different microbes can be found
and what they may be up to.
It will be a useful tour guide
for the next visitors!

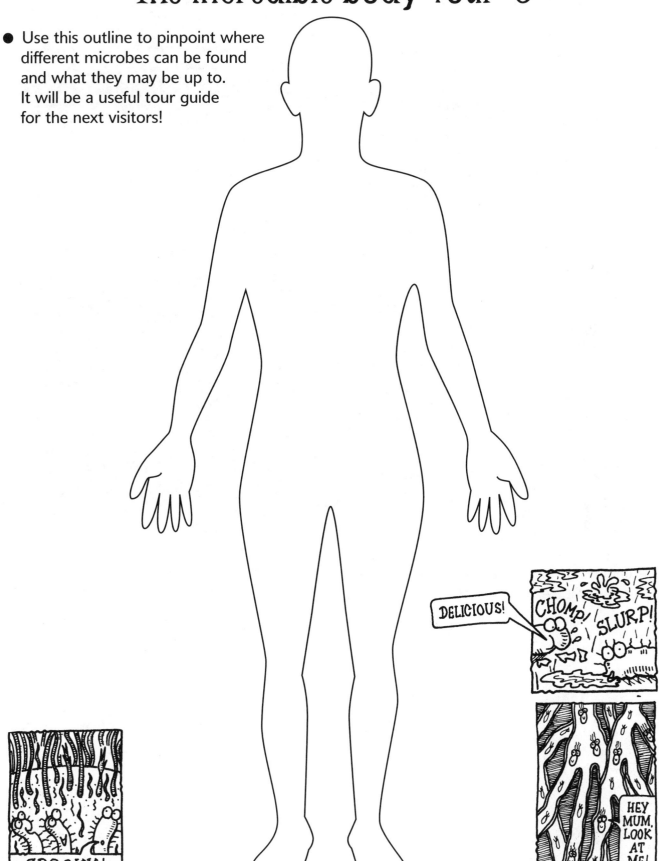

NAME _____   DATE _____

House of horrors

Hundreds of years ago a writer called Erasmus looked at his mate's house and said it was...

...a collection of spit, vomit, urine of dogs and men, beer, scraps of fish and other filthiness not to be named.

● But is *your* house any better when you look closely?

● Write a play to warn people about the microscopic horrors in their homes. Scene 1 has been started for you...

Scene 1: Mrs Mopp-Bucket's house. Mrs M-B and her cat are in the lounge.

MRS M-B: (wiping her table with a dirty rag) Well, Tiddles, time for a cuppa I reckon, nearly finished me cleanin' now!

MICROBE 1: (to audience) That's what she thinks!

MICROBE 2: Yeah, I just hopped off that mite-ridden cat of hers, very tasty...

THE HORRIBLE SCIENCE

ERK! YIKES! HELP! YUK! UGH!

NOT-VERY-IDEAL HOME EXHIBITION

BEDROOM Up to 2,000,000 mites in a double bed.

BEDROOM Red spider mite sneaks in from the garden to spend the winter indoors.

KITCHEN Flour mites snack on your breakfast cereal

BEDROOM Mangy cat fur caused by itch mite that burrows into Tiddles' flesh. (That's a cat-astrophe!)

LIVING ROOM Booklice feed on old books.

KITCHEN Bird mite refuses to budgie from your budgie

● What happens next? You decide!

NAME _____   DATE _____

Pillow problems

● Think you're safe from microbes when you're asleep? Think again! But don't worry, they don't do us much harm – unless you forget to clean and give them more dirt to feed on!

Let's imagine a dust mite wrote letters to her friend on the carpet. OK, I know this is a mite silly – after all I expect dust mites use mobile phones these days...

To Cara Petmite,
The carpet.

The Pillow.

Dear Cara,
Greetings from Pillowtown! It's comfy here and everything's fine. Trouble is a giant human insists on getting into bed with us every night and he snores! Mind you, the night life's great - there's 40,000 of us and I've got loads of mites. How's things with you?
Your mite,
Pilla Mite

← SOME OF MY MITES

Dear Cara,
As I was saying it's great - I've got the whole family with me including grandma and great grandma. Great-great-grandma's dead now but I see her mouldering body every time I go for a poo. And there's loads of food!
   Actually that's all down to the human I mentioned. The human lays on dead skin and grease and tasty dried dribble for us to eat. Is that generous or what? And the human even keeps us warm - so mustn't grumble!
Write soon!
Pilla

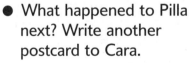
DEAD SKIN

CHOMP!

Dear Cara,
A terrible day! And it started so well - the cat slept on the pillow and left delicious globs of dried spit for our breakfast! The interesting fishy flavour makes a change from all that dead skin! Anyway, I puffed out a bit of gas PUFF from my bum (no it wasn't a fart, silly, it was a chemical signal to the family to come and eat) and I saw the huge jaws...
   A cheyletus. I don't have to tell you what these bugs do to us dust mites! It was after me but I got away. It grabbed my little sister and gobbled her up! I always used to argue with my sister but she went down a treat with the monster. Well, if I can't be safe in my own bed where can I be safe? I've crawled into the human's clothes and when the human gets into them I'm off to seek my fortune. See you on the carpet.
Your mite,   Pilla   BYE!

DRIBBLE!

● What happened to Pilla next? Write another postcard to Cara.

The microbe good food guide 1

Your house is *bulging* with bacteria. They're oozing over the furniture and slurping into the wallpaper and in the kitchen they're slobbering and squelching in your food. Dinner anyone?

THE MICROBE GOOD FOOD GUIDE...
By Mike Robe

Hi micro-munchers! There's nothing that we bacteria like better than a little nibble of nosh but we all suffer little dinner-time disasters. I'll never forget the day I tried to eat disinfectant! Anyway, here's our guide to the smartest and cheapest places to eat out as sampled by our team of inspectors — the slime squad!

A word about safety...
Safety is very important! Every year billions of bacteria suffer fatal accidents which could have been prevented by a little safety awareness. Things to beware of when eating out...

1 BLEACH Run a mile – and if you can't manage a mile, you'd better squirm a few millimetres. BLEACH WILL KILL YOU INSTANTLY!

2 SALT Don't eat too much of this. You'll find that your body will suck in water to dilute the salt and you'll explode!

THE KITCHEN BIN BISTRO

The classic eatery! A must for all gourmet bacteria. Easily the most wide-ranging menu, plus old favourites such as "cat food and cold mashed potato cottage pie" and "dad's cooking's gone wrong again" and that all-time favourite "last night's leftover curry". For pudding why not try slimy yoghurt scum? Recommended!

THE DISHCLOTH DINER

A cheap and cheerful watering hole with a smelly atmosphere all of its own. Here you can relax in the moist surroundings and dine on a delightful range of dishes including mouldy breadcrumb surprise and greasy fat soup.

THE COLD STEW CAFÉ

Delicious boiled meat and vegetables proved easy to digest with just a sprinkling of salt (but thankfully not enough to spoil the taste). There were delicious and tempting extras on offer such as "fresh fungi and mite-poo pudding". No wonder the restaurant was packed with bacteria! Recommended!

NAME _____ DATE _____

The microbe good food guide 2

- How should we handle food when we store, handle, prepare and serve it?

- Design a leaflet to help people understand the rules for handling food and why it is important to be careful.

Ideas for my information leaflet

HEADINGS

INFORMATION

PICTURES/DIAGRAMS

WARNINGS

THE TIN CAN HOTEL (guests only)

No bacteria are allowed past the strong metal walls! Conditions inside are said to be grim with no atmosphere at all! Actually we found out that bacteria do eat there but they're guests and sometimes they trash the place and cause nasty stinks.

~ SCIENTIFIC NOTE ~
These bacteria don't need oxygen to live.

THE GOLDEN EGG

The chemicals on the staff were a really hard-boiled lot and made us feel unwelcome – and that's no yolk – er, joke. One of our team was so badly treated that she dissolved! Best avoided.

~ SCIENTIFIC NOTE ~
Eggs contain chemicals that dissolve bacteria.

THE ICE-CREAM PARLOUR

I'm afraid this was another eatery that didn't live up to its initial promise. Although there was delicious fat on the menu the service was rather cold and eventually we felt we were being frozen out.

NAME _____   DATE _____

YUCKY YEAST 1

- Micro-organisms feed and grow but what do they need to do this?

What we need (equipment)
- Dried or fresh yeast (1 teaspoon)
- Warm water
- Sugar (half a teaspoon)
- Beaker
- Straight balloon
- Test tube

What we did (method)

_____

_____

_____

_____

What we think will happen (prediction)

_____

_____

What happened (results)

Time	Observation
0	
30 mins	
60 mins	
90 mins	
120 mins	
150 mins	
180 mins	

I'M HAVING TROUBLE WITH MY HYPOTHESIS

SHALL I CALL A DOCTOR?

Answer: NO. A hypothesis is the posh word for a scientific idea that hasn't been proven by an experiment.

My diagram

Before

After 180 mins

NAME _____   DATE _____

YUCKY YEAST 2

● What do you think yeast does to bread dough?

Equipment

1 tablespoon sugar	measuring jug
1 teaspoon dried yeast	weighing scales
200ml of warm water	two mixing bowls
300g plain flour	labels
clear beakers	pens

● The method below is all mixed up! Cut out the instructions and re-order them before starting.

Could this happen? What do you think?

BLAST!

a) Mix the remaining flour, water and sugar together to form 'Dough ball 2 – no yeast'.

b) Measure the height of the dough and put your observation in the database.

e) Measure them every quarter of an hour.

c) Put the dough balls in a warm place.

d) Measure 150g flour into a mixing bowl.

f) Add the yeast and half a tablespoon of sugar to 100ml of warm water.

g) Add the yeast mixture to the flour and mix it up. This will be 'Dough ball 1 – with yeast'.

h) Weigh the dough balls to check they are the same size. Put them in a beaker each and label the beakers.

● What do you think will happen? _____

_____

_____

_____

NAME _____   DATE _____

YUCKY YEAST 3

Time	Height of the dough	
	Dough ball 1 – with yeast	Dough ball 2 – no yeast
0 mins		
15 mins		
30 mins		
45 mins		
60 mins		

● What was the average measurement at the following times?

      0 mins   15 mins   30 mins   45 mins   60 mins

● Draw a line graph below to show this information. The x-axis should show the measurement; the y-axis should show the time scale.

WARNING!
● Don't eat the dough! It's for microbes only!

DELICIOUS! CHOMP! SLURP!

● What differences do you notice? What effect do you think yeast has on dough?

● Repeat the experiment, but put the dough balls in a cold place. What do you notice?

NAME _____   DATE _____

Dreadful decay

Micro-organisms can make things decay. When living things die they decay ... and that includes plants and humans!

● Which of these things will decay and which won't? Draw them, think about it and put a circle around the items that you think will decay.

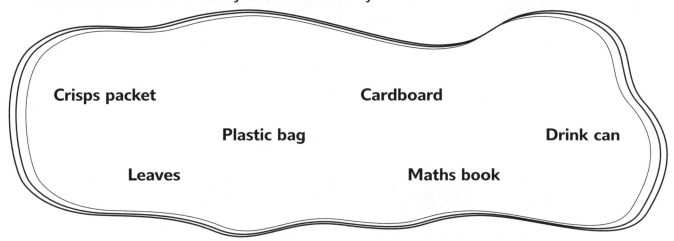

Crisps packet   Cardboard

Plastic bag   Drink can

Leaves   Maths book

● Do an experiment to test whether your predictions are correct.

● Record your observations in a table like this.

Item	Week 1	Week 2	Week 3	Week 4	Week 5	Week 6

● Use the following headings to write up your experiment.

WHAT WE PUT IN OUR DECAY BAG

WHAT WE DID WITH IT

WHAT WE THINK WILL HAPPEN

WHAT WE NOTICED

WHAT WE DISCOVERED

NAME _____ DATE _____

Beware of the bathroom 1

Come to the HORRIBLE SCIENCE MICRO-SAFARI PARK!

Lots of fun for all the family... in fact it's so much fun you won't be able to get them out of the bathroom even when you want to go to the toilet!

❶ EXPLORE THE EXCITING BLACK MOULD FOREST! The black spots you can see are actually the structures that make spores to make more black moulds whilst the little feeding tubes underneath eat your bathroom!

OOER!

❷ GO SCUBA DIVING in the romantic sink overflow – it's the place in the bathroom which has more germs than any other!

❸ CLIMB THE TOOTHBRUSH! It's crawling with germs – if you're lucky you'll spot a mouth-amoeba eating the bacteria!

CHOMP!

❹ EXPLORE THE TOWELS for stray dust mites and demodex creatures.

MUNCH!

CHEW!

❺ THE DOOR KNOB is a wonderful place to spot germs especially after someone's had a poo and not washed their hands properly. (One in five toilet door knobs have tiny lumps of poo on.)

PHWOAR!

❻ FEEDING TIME AT THE SOAP BAR. If it's wet you should see lots of germs happily eating the soap!

❼ Round off your visit with a trip to the taps to be entertained by the amazing **TAP-DANCING BACTERIA!**

TAP! TAP! TAP! TAP!

❽ Grand finale: Marvel at the **TOILET FLUSH-FOUNTAIN** as it showers you with tiny droplets of water and pee and germs and lumps of poo...

FLUSH!

PLOP!

● What can we do to keep this wildlife at bay? Design your own cartoon strip and present it to your class.

<table>
<tr><td></td><td></td><td></td><td></td></tr>
<tr><td></td><td></td><td></td><td></td></tr>
</table>

NAME _____   DATE _____

Beware of the bathroom 2

Even soap can have its hazards!

NAME: Washing and germs

1 Most people think that soap kills germs, but in fact most people are wrong. Soap doesn't usually kill germs, but it does send them on a one-way trip to the sewer. Here's how...

ARGH!

2 Washing your hands in water won't get rid of germs because they cling to the greasy surface of the skin. The water and grease don't mix so nothing happens.

CLING!

GERMS

GREASE

3 Tiny bits of soap (scientists call them molecules) consist of a "head" containing sodium and a "tail" made of chemicals called hydrocarbons (hi-dro-car-bons).

SOAP MOLECULE ← HEAD ← TAIL

This allows the water to wash grease, soap and germs down the plug hole!

HEAD REMAINS IN THE WATER

GREASE

TAIL STICKS IN THE GREASE

MONSTROUS DETAILS: Soap can also contain...

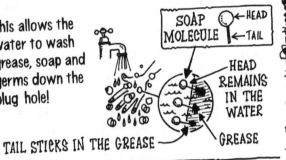

AIR BUBBLES

SMELLY FAT FROM A DEAD PIG

NICE PONG

A VERY WHITE CHEMICAL CALLED TITANIUM DIOXIDE TO GIVE A NICE CLEAN COLOUR

PERFUME SO YOU DON'T SMELL THE FAT

Fancy a quick scrub?

TERROR IN THE TOILET

GRRR!

If bacteria are getting under your skin or on your skin or up your nose or anywhere else, what should you do?
a) Pick your nose and spots.
b) Get someone else to pick your nose and spots.
c) Wash the bacteria off.

● Design a poster to help younger children to understand why it is important to wash your hands.

My poster ideas

Slogan:

Picture:

Warning:

Information to include:

Bet you never knew!
The soap will make bubbles on your hands as layers of soap and water trap air. Oh, so you've noticed? Well, take a good look at the surface of the bubble. At just 50 micrometres thick – it's thinner than a stick insect on a diet. It's actually one of the thinnest things you can see without a microscope.

NAME _____   DATE _____

Mixed-up microbes quiz

This quiz is so easy that you're even told what the answers are! Trouble is, the letters in the answers are muddled up so you've got to work out what they say!

1 Whenever you ride your bike the tyres leave tiny microscopic traces of melted ... REBRUB.

2 A fungus makes microscopic seeds called spores. When the sun shines they go dark just like you do when you get a ... STUNNA.

3 When you go outside your hair, your clothes and the snot in your nose become coated in thousands of microscopic bits of rock half the width of a hair. They're known as ... TRIG.

4 At the heart of every raindrop is a microscopic speck of dust. Some of this dust fell to Earth from ... ROUTE CAPES.

5 Look at a spider's web under a microscope and you'll see tiny lumps of ... GUEL.

6 All the tiny bits of dirt and dead skin that you've washed off your hair in your life would weigh more than your ... HOWLE ODBY.

7 In 1848 scientist John Queckett peered through his microscope at a scrap of leather that had been nailed to a church door. He was shocked to discover it was really ... UNHAM INKS.

UNHAM INKS! THAT'S DISGUSTING!

● Now try some mixed up questions on your partner.

● Don't be afraid of asking your teacher some really tough questions as well!

My questions

Answers:

1 No, not *rhubarb* – it's RUBBER. When your tyres touch the road a tiny surface layer 0.025mm thick melts – so in fact your wheel slides over the ground! The tyre cools immediately as the wheel turns away from the road but microscopic traces of rubber remain stuck to the tarmac. When your tyre has lost lots of rubber it looks worn and tyred, I mean tired.

2 Are you stunned? It's a SUNTAN. Yes, fungal spores get suntans and the chemical that makes this dark colour is melanin – the same substance that makes the dark colour in human skin!

3 Yes, it's a TRIGY question. It's GRIT, made up of finely ground-up rock or sand just 0.03mm in size that's blown on the wind. Some grit comes from deserts or erupting volcanoes on the other side of the world! If it gets in your pudding you could have a bit of desert in your dessert!

4 Every day millions of specks of dust about 0.002mm across fall to Earth from OUTER SPACE. Inside a cloud drops of rain form around the dust and when a raindrop plops down the back of your neck you could be making contact with a 4.7 billion-year-old lump of alien rock! It's even older than your dad's favourite music – that's just ancient rock.

5 Do they serve GUEL in your school dinners? Actually, it's GLUE to stick insects to the web. Did you know that spider's silk is one of the strongest materials in the world – yet a spider's web that stretched around the world would weigh no more than an orange?

6 Don't "HOWL ODDLY" – it's WHOLE BODY! In just one year you could collect 3kg of grotty, greasy gunk from your hair. You could fill a small bucket and butter your sandwiches with it!

7 What do you INK this stuff is? It turned out to be HUMAN SKIN cut from a dead Viking 900 years before. Well, I'm sure the Viking was really cut up about that.

WHO INVENTED THE MICROSCOPE?